The Black Arrow Rocket

A history of a satellite launch vehicle and its engines

Douglas Millard

Science Museum

Published 2001 by NMSI Trading Ltd,
Science Museum, Exhibition Road, London SW7 2DD.

British Library Cataloguing-in-Publication Data
A catalogue record for this publication is available from the British Library

Set in Postscript Monotype Plantin by Jerry Fowler
Printed in Belgium by Snoeck-Ducaju & Zoon
Cover artwork by Jerry Fowler

ISBN 1 900747 41 3

Website: http://www.nmsi.ac.uk

Contents

Acknowledgements

There were many individuals who assisted in some way in the production of this book. I would particularly like to thank the following:

Doron Swade, Robert Bud and Tim Boon for support and suggestions.

Ela Ginalska, Lawrence Ahlemeyer and Jerry Fowler for converting drafts into reality.

Dave Exton, Jenny Hills and especially Claire Richardson for some wonderful photography.

Kevin Royal, Rhiannan Sullivan and Chris Rowlin for processing the picture captions so quickly.

Matthew Applegate, Keith Brown, Ian Williams, Jon Hobbs and Neil Grey for working so easily and helpfully with some very heavy artefacts.

Brian Bradfield and Bob Townsend for working their magic on the artefacts' patina of age.

Jim Scragg, Ray Wheeler, Roy Dommett, David Andrews, John Scott-Scott and John Harlow for mining their memories and checking the details.

Margaret Pierce, David Cheek, Steve Tutton, Ian Moule, Nick Hill, Richard Williams (who supplied the picture of the R3 launch on page 49) and Robin Loader for various acts of kindness and assistance.

Clare Davies of the RAF Museum, Cosford, who supplied the picture of the Alpha engine on page 34.

And finally Stephanie, Edward and Daniel Millard for their patience with a preoccupied husband and dad.

Bibliography

For a first impression on some of Britain's post-war rocketry programmes, including Black Arrow:
Hill, C N, *A Vertical Empire: The History of the UK Rocket and Space Programme 1950–71* (London: Imperial College Press, 2001)

For a comprehensive and detailed overview of Black Arrow as one of the many vehicles tested and launched at Woomera:
Morton, P, *Fire Across the Desert: Woomera and the Anglo-Australian Joint Project, 1946–80,* (Canberra: Australian Government Publishing Service, 1989)

For a discussion of Black Arrow's place among the hundreds of land, sea, air and space vehicles produced by the Saunders-Roe company:
Tagg, A E and Wheeler, R L, *From Sea to Air: The Heritage of Sam Saunders* (Newport, Isle of Wight: Crossprint, 1989)

For a concise technical description of Black Arrow:
Gould, R D and Harlow, J, 'Black Arrow: the first British satellite launcher', *History of Rocketry and Astronautics*, 20, ed. Hunley, J D (American Astronautical Society, 1997), pp 257–273

For added details of the origins, design, development and operation of Black Arrow from first-hand experience:
Peatie, I W, 'The Black Arrow launch vehicle development programme', *Journal of the British Interplanetary Society*, 45, 4 (April 1992), pp 155–164
Robinson, H G R, 'The genesis of Black Arrow', *ibid.*, pp 149–154
Rolfe, J A and Green, S W, 'The solid propellant motors for Black Arrrow', *ibid.*, pp 165–172

For details of the actual and proposed Black Arrow satellites:
Day, B P, 'The Black Arrow satellites', *Journal of the British Interplanetary Society*, 45, 4 (April 1992), pp 173–178

For descriptions of the entire Black Knight vehicle, which was the precursor of Black Arrow:
Andrews, D and Sunley, H, 'The Gamma rocket engines for Black Knight', *Journal of the British Interplanetary Society*, 43, 7 (July 1990), pp 301–310
Andrews, D, 'Advantages of hydrogen peroxide as a rocket oxidant', *ibid.*, pp 319–328
Becklake, E J, 'The history of the Black Knight rocket', *ibid.*, pp 283–290
Harlow, J, 'Black Knight upper stages', *ibid.*, pp 311–316
Robinson, H G R, 'Overview of the Black Knight project: Black Knight, its genesis', *ibid.*, pp 291–295
Robinson, H G R, 'Suggested developments of Black Knight', *ibid.*, pp 317–318
Scragg, J, 'A contractor's view of the Black Knight programme', *ibid.*, pp 297–300

For in-depth official discussion of why the Black Arrow programme was cancelled:
House of Commons, 'United Kingdom space activities', 5th Report from the Select Committee on Science and Technology (London: HMSO, October 1971)

For an excellent history and technical summary of both the Alpha and Beta engine designs:
Harlow, J, 'Alpha, Beta and the RTV-1: the development of early British liquid propellant rocket engines', *History of Rocketry and Astronautics*, 22, ed. Jung, P (American Astronautical Society, 1998), pp 173–201

Glossary

Ariane launch vehicle
Satellite launch vehicle developed by the European Space Agency.

Ballistic trajectory
The part of a missile or rocket flight that is unpowered and determined by the effects of gravity and atmospheric friction.

Cam-operated microswitches
Small switches activated by a series of projecting teeth set into a revolving mechanism.

Catalyst
A substance that speeds up a chemical reaction without taking part in the reaction or altering its products.

Combustion chamber
The part of a rocket engine where the propellants are ignited under high pressure.

Commonwealth
The group of nations built largely from those that comprised the former British empire.

Earth/Sun sensors
Detectors that respond to the direction of light from either the Sun or reflected from the surface of the Earth, in order to help orientate the satellite.

First-strike weapon
A weapon used first, rather than in response to an attack by the enemy.

Intercontinental ballistic missile
A missile with a range of at least 5500 km.

Intermediate-range ballistic missile
A missile with a range of between 500 and 5500 km.

Ionised gas
A gas whose molecules have become either positively charged as a result of losing electrons, or negatively charged as a result of gaining electrons.

Low Earth orbit
An orbit of the Earth at an altitude between 320 and 800 km.

One-megaton nuclear warhead
A nuclear explosive device having the destructive power equivalent to 1,000,000 tonnes of conventional explosive.

Orbital inclination
The angle between the plane of a satellite's orbit and the plane of the Earth's equator.

Pre-emptive nuclear strike
An attack with nuclear weapons designed to surprise the enemy.

Strategic nuclear deterrent
A defensive capability using nuclear weapons that can strike targets in the enemy's heartland, as opposed to on the battlefield.

Ventral fin
An aerodynamic fin sited on the underside of the vehicle.

Introduction

R4 is the last of the Black Arrow space rockets. It hangs majestically in the Science Museum, its streamlined silver skin cold and its formidable engines silent. They belch no flame, produce no thunder, merely hint at what they might unleash. The rocket's predecessor, Black Arrow R3, carried the Prospero satellite into orbit in 1971. With a few new components and a full load of propellants, R4 could also be readied for launch: the vehicle on display is virtually intact. Instead, it remains static, a mute reminder of the awesome power of twentieth-century technology, a technology that released us from Earth's clutches and propelled us into orbit. This is the story of how R4 was sent to the Museum rather than into space.

During the late 1940s and 1950s, Britain's defence chiefs were concerned with minimising the response time of the country's armed forces in the event of an attack by the Soviet Union. Rocket propulsion, whether applied to aircraft, guided missiles or ballistic missiles, assisted in meeting this need and Britain engaged in a wide-ranging series of rocketry research programmes. Rocket propulsion would also enable space flight, which had been predicted by the nineteenth-century Russian scientist Konstantin Tsiolkovsky. When the Soviet Union launched the world's first artificial satellite, Sputnik 1, in 1957 using a converted ballistic missile, it was clear that those other nations having long-range missile programmes could also, in principle, launch their own satellites. At the time, the United States and Britain were the only other nations in a position to do so.

Britain held back. The final decision to build the national satellite launch vehicle called Black Arrow was not taken until 1966. By the time the Black Arrow R3 vehicle launched Prospero in 1971, four other countries had already followed the Soviet Union's example and launched their own satellites. Stranger still, R3 was to be the first and last orbital launch of a Black Arrow vehicle: the British government had already cancelled the programme. This book also considers why this turnaround might have happened.

A focus of the book's narrative is Black Arrow's engines. These were products of the Cold War, that period after the Second World War when the military forces of East and West faced each other in nuclear stalemate. The book looks at how these engines were developed from Britain's defence programmes and illustrates this process through extensive references to the Space Technology and Aircraft Propulsion collections of the Science Museum. Some of the artefacts, Black Arrow R4 and the Messerschmitt Me 163 included, are on public display in the Museum, while the others are in store and can be inspected by appointment. This particular history is therefore an artefact-led one and serves also as a guide to the Science Museum's holdings in the relevant areas. It makes no claim to represent alternative narratives and especially those that would undoubtedly provide greater insights into the technology of the Black Arrow programme and the wider story of Britain's role in the Cold War.

The never-used Black Arrow R4 vehicle in the Science Museum's Space *gallery. The X3 satellite flight spare and* Waxwing *apogee motor can be seen ahaead of the rocket's open fairings. (Science & Society Picture Library)*

1 From missiles to spaceflight

1.1 The first satellites

The space age began on 4 October 1957, when the Soviet Union used a modified R7 intercontinental ballistic missile to launch the world's first artificial satellite, Sputnik 1 (Figure 1.1). Around the world, people listened in awe to the bleeps from Sputnik's radio transmitter. Those in the United States listened in anger; they had expected their country to be the first to launch a satellite. Other countries had expected the USA to be first too (Figures 1.2 and 1.3). One month later, the Soviet Union triumphed again, when Sputnik 2 and its crew of one, Laika the dog, were launched into space.

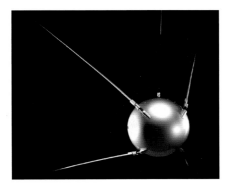

Figure 1.1 Sputnik 1 satellite (replica), c. 1957. Sputnik 1 was a hollow aluminium sphere, 580 mm in diameter, with four projecting radio antennas. It contained batteries and a simple transmitter. Its designer, Sergei Korolev, criticised a colleague for the poor quality of an exhibition mock-up because 'this ball will be exhibited in museums'! The replica shown here was made by the Science Museum (Inventory No. 1985-1665). (Science & Society Picture Library)

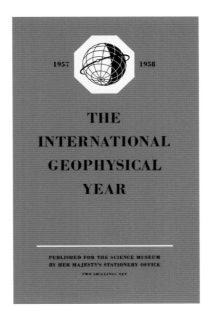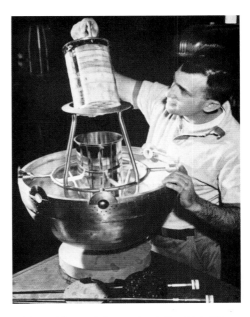

Figures 1.2 and 1.3 Cover and illustration from the Science Museum's International Geophysical Year Exhibition handbook, 1957. The International Geophysical Year of 1957–58 was conceived by Dr L V Berkner of the United States. One of its objectives was to launch the world's first artificial satellite. Western countries expected that the United States would be the first to achieve this, with the Vanguard satellite, shown being assembled in the photograph. The author of the handbook also assumed the United States would be first. (US State Department)

The Royal Aircraft Establishment was founded in 1918 and changed its name to the Royal Aerospace Establishment in 1988. In 1991 it became part of the Defence Research Agency, which was renamed the Defence Evaluation Research Agency in 1995, and then the Defence Science and Technology Laboratories in 2001.

The Guided Projectile Establishment was set up in 1946. It became the Rocket Propulsion Department of the RAE the following year, and then changed its name to the Rocket Propulsion Establishment in 1958. From 1977 the establishment was part of the Propellants, Explosives and Rocket Research Establishment, which itself became part of Royal Ordnance plc in 1985. Since 1987 it has been part of the company now known as BAE Systems plc.

In December, the United States' own attempt to orbit a satellite failed: the Vanguard launch vehicle, developed by the navy, exploded on its launch pad. A second attempt also failed in January 1958. The USA eventually succeeded with the Explorer 1 satellite, launched on 31 January 1958. This launch – like those of the Soviet Union – used a modified missile, in this case Juno 1, a version of the Jupiter C developed by the US Army.

1.2 Blue Streak

In Britain, people's reaction to Sputnik 1 was less frenzied than in the United States. Nevertheless, within days of the satellite's launch, MPs were questioning the Conservative government of Harold Macmillan on the subject. They wanted to know whether Britain would follow the Soviet Union's example and convert its ballistic missiles into satellite launchers. Besides the United States, Britain was the only other nation that could build satellite launchers at that time.

Britain was two years into its Blue Streak programme. Blue Streak was an intermediate range ballistic missile that would be capable of delivering a one-megaton nuclear warhead to its target (Figure 1.4). It would be launched from underground silos in the south and east of England and climb above the Earth's atmosphere. Then, it would re-enter the atmosphere in a ballistic trajectory to strike strategic targets in the Soviet Union. Blue Streak was not intended as a first-strike weapon; it would only be launched in response to an incoming Soviet missile strike.

1.3 Black Knight

Scientists trying to predict the behaviour of Blue Streak's warhead as it re-entered the atmosphere had needed an intensive research programme. They knew little of the warhead's likely performance in flight. The research had had to determine the type of material the warhead should be made out of and in what shape. To enable this work, Britain had developed a test missile called Black Knight (Figures 1.5 and 1.6). Researchers launched Black Knight vehicles at steep angles (Figure 1.7), with test re-entry heads of different shapes and materials (Figure 1.8). As the re-entry heads re-entered the atmosphere, the researchers monitored their behaviour and used the information to design the operational warhead for Blue Streak.

Black Knight was a far smaller rocket vehicle than Blue Streak. It was not nearly powerful enough to launch a satellite. The same was true of Blue Streak itself, despite its greater size. But there was a way in which Britain could, in theory, use these rockets to build a satellite launch vehicle. The idea was to combine Blue Streak and Black Knight as the first and second stages of a larger vehicle, and then add a small third stage. Britain's main defence research centre, the Royal Aircraft Establishment

Figure 1.4 An early Blue Streak development vehicle being raised into position for testing at De Havilland Propellers' Hatfield site in Hertfordshire, England, c. 1959. Blue Streak was based on the United States' Atlas missile, and was fitted with RZ-12 engines that burned kerosene in liquid oxygen. Transatlantic agreements allowed British companies, helped by the Royal Aircraft Establishment, to acquire information from their United States equivalents. This enabled these companies to develop the Blue Streak vehicle. De Havilland Propellers Ltd liaised with Convair on the vehicle itself, while Rolls-Royce exchanged information with the Rocketdyne division of North America Aviation. (Astrium)

(RAE), performed technical studies to see how such a Blue Streak/Black Knight combination might be built. This was why the Macmillan government was asked questions following the launch of Sputnik 1 – Britain had the potential to adapt its missiles for spaceflight.

However, the government made no policy commitment on any aspect of space exploration until 1959. The delay frustrated those scientists, engineers, industrialists and commentators who felt that Britain should be taking a more active role in the new field of space exploration. Prime Minister Macmillan then announced that Britain would embark upon a scientific satellite programme, but he did not say what kind of vehicle would be used to launch the satellites. Britain might use a vehicle developed for the missile programme, but might also consider a collaborative effort with the United States, with Britain's Commonwealth or with other countries. In reality, a United States offer of its Scout vehicle to launch satellites had prompted Macmillan's space policy announcement in the first place; by autumn 1959, plans were well advanced to take advantage of the offer. This meant that the Blue Streak/Black Knight studies remained on the drawing board. However, the Macmillan government would also have been aware of developments elsewhere, which meant that Blue Streak/Black Knight was not forgotten.

1.4 Problems with Blue Streak

Blue Streak was intended as a retaliatory weapon: it would only be used if the Soviet Union launched a missile attack on Britain first. But the Soviet Union's forces were so vastly superior to Britain's, that the damage caused by a Soviet attack would dwarf any damage that Britain's Blue Streak could inflict in retaliation. The deterrent factor of Blue Streak was built on the calculation that if just some of the Blue Streak missiles could penetrate Soviet defences, then the Soviet Union might hesitate from launching an attack first.

However, if Blue Streak was shown to be vulnerable to such a Soviet first strike, its credibility as a retaliatory weapon would be seriously undermined. Retaining Blue Streak in these circumstances would indicate that British military policy had shifted from being defensive in nature to being offensive. This would increase the likelihood of the Soviet Union launching a pre-emptive nuclear strike to destroy Britain's offensive capability. In other words, in a worsening international situation in the run-up to war, the Soviet Union would be more likely to launch a massive pre-emptive nuclear strike on Britain if an 'offensive' Blue Streak system was retained.

By 1960, Britain's defence chiefs had concluded that Blue Streak *was* vulnerable. This meant that it could only be retained as an offensive weapon and, given that there were alternative US systems now available, should be cancelled. The Macmillan government therefore decided to abandon Blue Streak in April 1960. Plans were

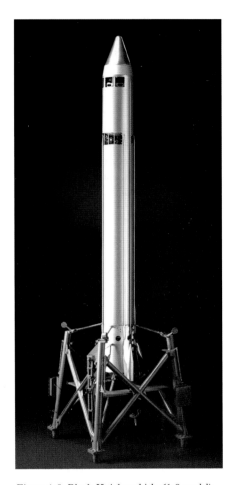

Figure 1.5 *Black Knight vehicle (1:8 model),* *c. 1957. Black Knight was originally designed to accelerate a re-entry head back into the atmosphere at speeds of about 3.6 km/s. The first flights were successful and later programmes called Gaslight and Dazzle were completed with help from the United States. The model shown here was made at the Royal Aircraft Establishment (Inventory No. 1974-236). (Science & Society Picture Library)*

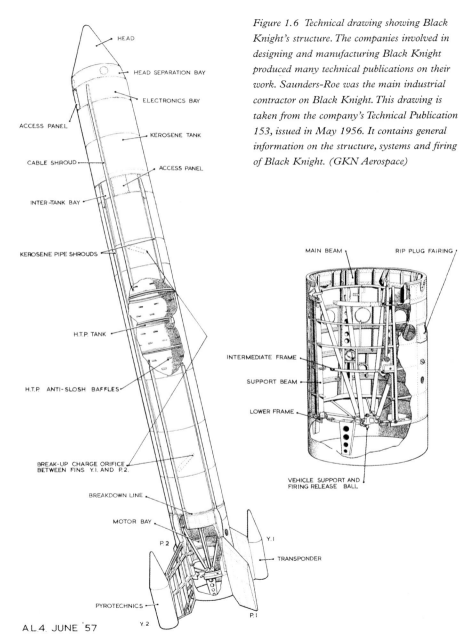

HEAD

HEAD SEPARATION BAY

ELECTRONICS BAY

ACCESS PANEL

KEROSENE TANK

CABLE SHROUD

ACCESS PANEL

INTER-TANK BAY

KEROSENE PIPE SHROUDS

H.T.P. TANK

H.T.P. ANTI-SLOSH BAFFLES

BREAK-UP CHARGE ORIFICE BETWEEN FINS Y.I. AND P.2.

BREAKDOWN LINE

MOTOR BAY

P.2

Y.I

TRANSPONDER

PYROTECHNICS

P.I

Y.2

A L 4 JUNE '57

MAIN BEAM

RIP PLUG FAIRING

INTERMEDIATE FRAME

SUPPORT BEAM

LOWER FRAME

VEHICLE SUPPORT AND FIRING RELEASE BALL

Figure 1.6 Technical drawing showing Black Knight's structure. The companies involved in designing and manufacturing Black Knight produced many technical publications on their work. Saunders-Roe was the main industrial contractor on Black Knight. This drawing is taken from the company's Technical Publication 153, issued in May 1956. It contains general information on the structure, systems and firing of Black Knight. (GKN Aerospace)

made to replace it with the United States' Skybolt missile system, but tests showed that its technology was faulty. Macmillan then had negotiations with US President John F Kennedy, who agreed to sell Britain the Polaris submarine-launched ballistic missile system instead.

1.5 Black Prince

Although Blue Streak now had no future as a missile, British scientists intensified their work to incorporate it in a Blue Streak/Black Knight satellite launch vehicle. The project was given a name: Black Prince (Figure 1.9). The vehicle would comprise an almost unchanged Blue Streak for its first stage, a slightly modified Black Knight for its second stage and a third based on the Bristol Siddeley PR-38 rocket engine. Black Prince would be capable of launching two types of satellites: a 1750 lb (794 kg) satellite into a 300 mile (480 km) orbit and a 220 lb (100 kg) satellite into an elliptical orbit with a maximum altitude of 100,000 miles (160,000 km).

Black Prince became a collaborative venture between the RAE, Saunders Roe Ltd (the prime industrial contractor for Black Knight) and Bristol Siddeley Ltd (the Black Knight engine contractor). These organisations were keen that the knowledge and expertise gained in the Blue Streak and Black Knight programmes should be redirected into a new and challenging project to launch satellites. The government also backed the scheme – in as far as it would safeguard jobs, salvage some of the money invested in Blue Streak and Black Knight and maintain Britain's prowess in long-range rocket technology. But the government was less committed to the idea of a satellite launch system: it was not convinced that a national satellite launch programme was needed, since it would duplicate a capability that the United States was already offering to Britain. Despite the political benefits, the government remained wary of allocating further public funds to the Black Prince proposal and instead looked for other ways to deal with the legacy of its missile programme.

Hoping to share the costs of development, the government asked France whether it would be interested in joining the Black Prince project. The response was encouraging, but France made it clear that the vehicle's second stage should be French. The British government was prepared to accept this – perhaps because ministers thought that more cooperation with European countries would aid Britain's hopes of joining the Common Market. France remained unhappy, however, about the way the proposal allocated costs between the two countries. It also objected because Britain refused to share Blue Streak's guidance and re-entry technologies with France. Britain was unable to share this information because it was joint United States/British knowledge and the United States was concerned about the spread of missile technologies internationally.

Figure 1.7 *Sketch illustrating the trajectory of Black Knight, c. 1957. This sketch shows the almost vertical ascent and descent of the Black Knight vehicles. The steep trajectory meant that the impact zone for the re-entry head could be kept relatively close to the launch site. This allowed the Black Knight programme to start quickly, since there would be no need for new safety measures to protect people and property outside the designated test area. It also allowed existing tracking techniques to be used during the ascent: optical telescopes to an altitude of 6 km, then radar up to 128 km. (Crown copyright)*

Figure 1.8 *Black Knight re-entry head, c. 1960. This near-conical re-entry head is made of Durestos, a composite of asbestos held in a phenolic resin. As it re-entered the atmosphere, the head's surface would have become hot and burned or 'ablated' away, allowing a lower internal temperature to be maintained. A section of the head has been removed to reveal instrumen-tation that measured the head's temperature, its acceleration and the accuracy of signals received from the ground (Inventory No. 1974-304). (Science & Society Picture Library)*

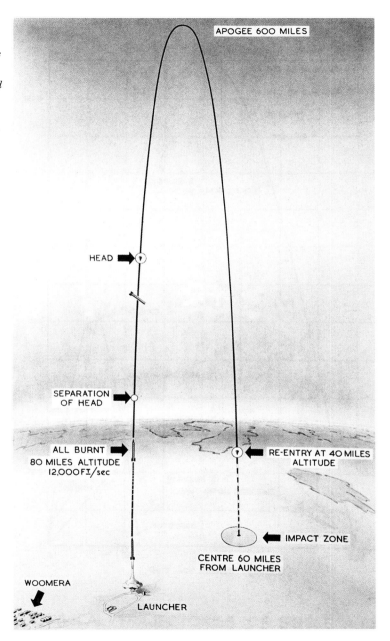

APOGEE 600 MILES

HEAD

SEPARATION
OF HEAD

ALL BURNT
80 MILES ALTITUDE
12,000 FT/sec

RE-ENTRY AT 40 MILES
ALTITUDE

IMPACT ZONE

CENTRE 60 MILES
FROM LAUNCHER

WOOMERA

LAUNCHER

Figure 1.9 Technical drawing comparing Black Prince to Blue Streak and Black Knight. While Blue Streak was virtually unchanged as Black Prince's first stage, Black Knight was expanded in diameter from 3 ft (0.91 m) to 4 ft 6 in (1.37 m). This allowed it to carry more propellants and so increased its performance. The propellant capacity of the new third stage could be altered, depending on the type of satellite to be launched. This drawing is taken from Saunders-Roe's Technical Publication 435, issued in May 1960. (GKN Aerospace)

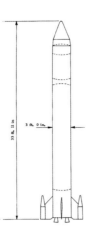

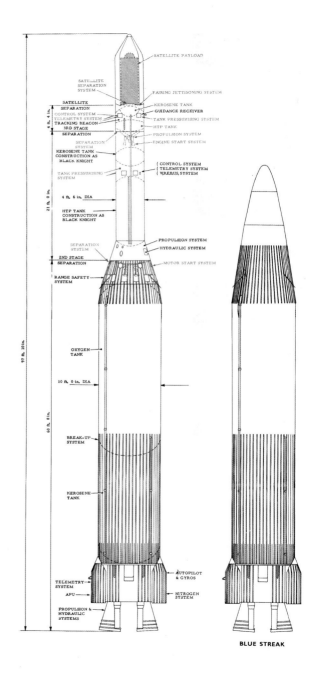

Figure 1.10 Model of the European Launcher Development Organisation's Europa vehicle, c. 1964. This model, made out of polished stainless steel, accurately portrays the Europa's external design. The Europa development teams would have referred to it during their work and it would have been displayed at exhibitions. (Science & Society Picture Library)

1.6 Europa

Peter Thorneycroft, Britain's Minister of Aviation, travelled back and forth between London and Paris, in an attempt to keep the Black Prince project going. But, by the end of 1960, France appeared to be losing interest in the satellite launch vehicle proposal altogether. And then, in January 1961, the French government suddenly dropped its objections. France was now ready to come in on the joint project, and was no longer demanding access to Blue Streak's sensitive technologies. The reversal came shortly after one of Harold Macmillan's regular meetings with the French president, Charles de Gaulle. It perhaps owed something to Macmillan's close working knowledge of de Gaulle, which went back to their days of cooperation in the Second World War, and the French president's own aims for France and Europe in the 1960s.

With Britain and France now in agreement, officials held further negotiations to bring other European nations on board. These talks enabled a European Satellite Launcher Organisation (ELDO) to be set up. ELDO was formally established in 1964, its main objective to build a three-stage satellite launch vehicle called Europa (Figure 1.10). Europa's first stage would be Blue Streak, its second stage the French Coralie and its third the German Astris. Italy would build the satellites.

Blue Streak had therefore been salvaged, but as part of a pan-European project, and with no role for Black Knight. It seemed that the big opportunity to develop an all-British satellite launch vehicle, following Blue Streak's cancellation, had been missed. This was not the end of the story, however.

1.7 New designs and Black Arrow

While the complex negotiations surrounding Blue Streak and ELDO had been going on, Britain's RAE had proposed two new launch vehicle designs. The first of these would extend the Black Knight programme. Already, the RAE and industry had produced two-stage versions of the original single-stage Black Knight vehicles. The second stages of these rockets were arranged so that they accelerated the warheads downwards as they re-entered the atmosphere (Figure 1.11). The RAE's proposed extension of this programme would use an enlarged and still more powerful Black Knight to launch a re-entry physics programme, code-named Crusade.

The second RAE proposal used as much Black Knight technology as possible in the production of a small satellite launch vehicle (Figure 1.12). This vehicle would be far smaller than Black Prince, but still aimed to provide Britain with an independent satellite launching capability. It would launch satellites of approximately 317 lb (144 kg) into low Earth orbits. These satellites would enable scientists to test prototype power, orientation, telemetry and other systems in the harsh space environment, rather than under the standard simulated conditions on the ground.

The proposal suggested that this chance to try out new space technologies on real satellites might help British satellite manufacturing companies to compete more effectively for foreign orders.

The RAE did not have sufficient funds to proceed with both proposals. The extended Black Knight programme was considered, but eventually rejected – military strategists now judged it unnecessary. That decision left the option of the satellite launch vehicle, and in autumn 1964, the new Minister of Aviation, Julian Amery, announced the start of its development. Britain was at least embarking upon its own space launcher programme. But, within weeks, the new programme was encountering difficulties.

Conservative Prime Minister Harold Macmillan had retired on health grounds in 1963, and his successor, Sir Alec Douglas-Home, called a general election in October 1964. The Labour party – led by Harold Wilson – won a narrow victory, but the new government immediately faced a growing economic crisis. Anxious to cut spending, ministers applied the brakes to the satellite launch vehicle project. They drew back from giving it the go-ahead, and instead would only grant it funds in a series of three-monthly holding contracts. There the situation rested for the entire lifetime of the Wilson government. The project was nearly cancelled – Wilson's Cabinet was unclear whether Britain needed it. In 1966, there was another general election, and the Labour government was returned to power with an increased majority. Towards the end of that year, the launch vehicle project, now publicly known as Black Arrow, was finally given the go-ahead. Its programme would be trimmed, however – the number of proposed test launches was reduced from five to three, to save money. Development would now proceed and the first launch was planned for 1968.

Black Arrow had survived, in part because its design was not too ambitious. Almost all the technology required for its development was already there. It was very similar to Black Knight, a vehicle that had been launched 22 times without a single major failure. The systems that Black Arrow would use were known, and their performance was predictable. Black Arrow would make maximum use of the existing Black Knight facilities, and the amount of new work required would be kept to an absolute minimum. As a result, the Wilson government was attracted by the project and saw it as a cost-effective way of developing a national satellite launch vehicle.

Black Arrow's engines were an example of the practicality of the rocket's design. They were variants of Black Knight's engines, which themselves drew on ten years of British rocketry research for defence purposes. The engines' propellant was concentrated (85 per cent) hydrogen peroxide, otherwise known as high-test peroxide (HTP). Britain had become a world leader in the use of this substance as a rocket propellant. This rocket-engine knowledge was the key technological factor that allowed Britain to contemplate building a satellite launch vehicle; it was also long-established expertise that had crossed national boundaries before arriving in Britain.

Figure 1.11 Black Knight vehicles 13 (foreground) and 14 (two-stage) on launch sites 5A and 5B respectively at Australia's Weapons Research Establishment. Black Knight 13 was launched in February 1961, Black Knight 14 in May 1961. The second stage of 14 was a Cuckoo 1b solid-propellant motor. This motor was 'inverted' on the Black Knight so that when fired it accelerated the re-entry head to greater velocities. All the Black Knight missions were launched from the WRE test range at Woomera, South Australia. (Crown copyright)

The next chapter describes how the ancestry of Black Arrow's engines can be traced back over many years – through a variety of British designs of the Cold War, via the German rocket-powered weapons of the Second World War – to the innovations of a German engineer in the mid-1930s.

Figure 1.12 An original drawing taken from the Royal Aircraft Establishment's report 'A small satellite launcher based on Black Knight technology', 1964. A comparison of this drawing with Figure 3.1 shows how mature the design of the vehicle that became Black Arrow was in 1964. A notable difference is in the shape of the 'apogee motor/rocket', which would propel the satellite to its required altitude and orbit. In this 1964 drawing it is depicted as a traditional cylindrical shape; in Figure 3.1 it is nearly spherical. This change was made to keep the amount of steel casing to an absolute minimum for a given amount of propellant contained within. (Crown copyright)

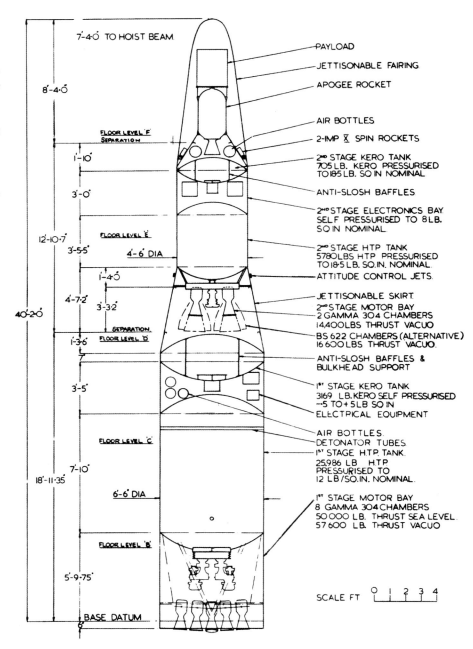

2 The dynasty of Black Arrow's engines

2.1 The convenience of HTP as a rocket-engine propellant

A rocket engine burns fuel in a supply of oxygen, just as a jet engine does. Both engines move forward in the direction opposite to their exhaust. This movement follows Isaac Newton's third law of motion, which says that to every action there is an equal and opposite reaction. But a rocket engine's exhaust is far stronger than a jet's, so it is said to produce a greater thrust. To achieve this greater thrust, oxygen must be fed into the combustion chamber of the rocket engine as a pressurised liquid; but a jet engine only needs oxygen at natural atmospheric pressure. A rocket engine must also burn its fuel at a far higher temperature and pressure.

Oxygen can be carried chemically into a rocket engine in a number of different liquid forms, including nitric acid, liquid oxygen itself and HTP. Concentrated nitric acid propellant is highly corrosive, which makes handling it especially hazardous. Liquid oxygen is an efficient rocket engine propellant, but it evaporates easily from tanks and pipework and has to be kept at a temperature of −183 °C. Blue Streak's liquid oxygen propellant could not be stored on board the missile, as it would eventually have leaked. Instead, it had to be pumped in immediately before launch; this process took seven minutes, by which time any incoming Soviet missile would have struck.

HTP, on the other hand, is relatively easy to handle and stays liquid at room temperature and pressure. Despite this, HTP must still be kept in scrupulously clean containers, as impurities will cause it to decompose into oxygen and water – and into steam if the heat generated in the decomposition is sufficient to vaporise the water (Figure 2.1). The most critical impurities, such as silver and certain permanganate salts, will cause HTP to decompose in an explosion. But it is this ease of decomposition that makes HTP such a useful rocket engine propellant.

2.2 'Cold' and 'hot' HTP engines

When catalysts that are metals or metal salts are used in an HTP rocket engine, large quantities of superheated steam can be generated and used to produce thrust. This thrust is achieved *without* the need for a fuel. In other words, the HTP acts as a 'monopropellant': the rocket thrust is generated by the HTP's own chemical decomposition, rather than as a result of burning fuel in it. Such fuel-less HTP engines are termed 'cold'.

In 1951, the De Havilland Engine Company used two Sprite cold HTP rocket engines (Figure 2.2) to boost the takeoff of its Comet airliner. These rocket units

Figure 2.1 Protective clothing for the handling of HTP, c. 1960. This worker has just been working on an HTP rocket-engine test site. He is wearing a protective suit made of PTFE-coated nylon fabric. Any residual HTP must be washed off with water to prevent it attacking the material. Ordinary clothing would smoulder and catch fire if HTP was spilled on it. (Rolls-Royce plc)

Figure 2.2 Sprite rocket engine, c. 1951. The De Havilland company built six Sprites for aircraft trials, but improved jet-engine design eventually made them redundant. During the early stages of the development programme, De Havilland flew a Lancastrian aircraft with three different types of engine: one pair of Merlin piston engines, one pair of Ghost turbojets and one pair of Walter 109-500 rocket engines (see Figure 2.3). The Sprite's HTP was decomposed with either calcium or sodium permanganate as the catalyst (Inventory No. 1962-104). (Science & Society Picture Library)

Figure 2.3 Walter 109-500 rocket engine, c. 1939. One engine would be strapped under each wing of the aircraft. When airborne, the rocket engines were jettisoned by parachute and reused. Six thousand units were built by the Heinkel company for use on various aircraft. The 109-500's HTP was decomposed by a calcium permanganate catalyst (Inventory No. 1985-2003). (Science & Society Picture Library)

Figure 2.4 Walter 109-509A rocket engine, c. 1943. This engine used a fuel mixture called 'C-Stoff', or C-substance, which consisted of methyl alcohol and hydrazine hydrate. C-Stoff also contained copper salts, which acted as the catalyst for the decomposition of the HTP (which was code-named 'T-Stoff'). Unlike the earlier 109-500 series, this engine relied on a turbo-pump to deliver the propellants to the combustion chamber; the pump itself was driven by the cold decomposition of HTP (Inventory No. 1993-306). (Science & Society Picture Library)

Figure 2.5 Messerschmitt Me 163 'Komet' aircraft, c. 1943. The Komets approached their targets at speeds greater than 1000 km/h, but succeeded in destroying only 13 Allied aircraft. Their descent was unpowered and they landed on a skid, as the undercarriage was jettisoned on takeoff (Inventory No. 1958-103). (Science & Society Picture Library)

added to the thrust of the aircraft's jet engines and were intended for use at high-altitude airports, where the air is thin and jet engines are inefficient. De Havilland based the Sprite on a German cold HTP engine, the 109-500 (Figure 2.3), which the company acquired at the end of the Second World War. This engine had been developed by Dr Hellmuth Walter and his company in 1939 to assist heavily-laden Heinkel bomber aircraft during takeoff.

But HTP can also act as the oxygen supply for a burning rocket fuel. Engines that use this principle are termed 'hot', because the fuel combustion reaction occurs at a higher temperature than that developed when HTP decomposes in a cold engine. Hot HTP engines are able to develop greater thrust. Also, the heat generated in the HTP decomposition will raise the fuel temperature above its 'flash point'. This will cause the fuel to combust automatically in the presence of the decomposed oxygen; therefore no special components will be needed to ignite the fuel.

2.3 The Walter 109-509 engine

Germany had increased its rocketry research programmes at the start of the Second World War, and the Walter Company designed a hot HTP engine, the RII 211.

The engine was produced in quantity as the Walter Type 109-509 (Figure 2.4), and propelled the revolutionary Messerschmitt Me 163b interceptor, otherwise known as the 'Komet' (Figure 2.5). These aircraft carried out surprise attacks on US bomber aircraft as they flew over Germany. Their great speed unsettled the Allied aircrews, but they proved relatively ineffectual as a weapon; their high speed meant they had only a single, brief chance to attack the US aircraft before they had passed by. The Me 263/Junkers 248 aircraft, which used the Walter 109-509C engine (Figure 2.6), was addressing this limitation when the war ended.

2.4 *The emigration of HTP rocket engine technology*

At the end of the war, Hellmuth Walter continued to work in Germany under supervision, so that Britain could learn more of his team's HTP expertise. He was then brought to Britain to work at the Admiralty Development Establishment at Barrow-in-Furness, Cumbria. There, he returned to his initial work with HTP on submarine propulsion systems.

Some of Walter's colleagues went to work at other British government research establishments, including the then-named Guided Projectile Establishment at Westcott, Buckinghamshire, and the Royal Aircraft Establishment. These engineers' knowledge became part of the expertise of the early post-war British rocket programme.

2.5 *The Alpha and Beta HTP engines*

The first British hot HTP rocket engine was the Alpha. It was designed and built at the RAE and was used to propel the Vickers transonic model aircraft to supersonic velocities. The Alpha burned a fuel mixture of methyl alcohol, hydrazine hydrate and water in its HTP. The injector head of the combustion chamber was based on that of the Walter 109-509 engine. Alpha was followed by Beta 1 and Beta 2, the first British rocket engines to use pump-pressurised systems (the high pressure in Alpha's systems had been maintained with nitrogen gas). Some of the Beta's HTP was rerouted in the engine so that, when it decomposed, the steam produced could be used to drive the engine's pump.

The Beta 1 engine (Figures 2.7–2.9) was developed by engineers at the Rocket Propulsion Department of the RAE, formerly the Guided Projectile Establishment, to launch the Fairey high-angle launch aircraft. This vehicle was inspired by the Natter, a Second World War German interceptor. The Natter was a manned, rocket-powered vehicle, and was launched vertically to attack incoming aircraft. Beta 2, a more powerful version of the engine, was used on development models of the Fairey Delta 1 supersonic fighter. The Beta design again drew heavily on German technology: its propellant pump was almost identical to that of the Walter 109-509A engine.

Figure 2.6 Walter 109-509C engine combustion chamber, c. 1945. The 109-509C was a two-chambered engine, and the smaller combustion chamber allowed the Me 263/Junkers 248 aircraft to have a degree of cruise control. This example of the smaller chamber has been sectioned to show its double skin. C-Stoff fuel was pumped between its two layers to keep it cool (Inventory No. 1993-0309). (Science & Society Picture Library)

Figure 2.7 A German engineer inspects a Beta 1 rocket engine before a static firing test at the Rocket Propulsion Department, Westcott, c. 1950. The Westcott site was acquired in 1946 as a disused Second World War RAF training station. For the next 50 years, it acted as Britain's main rocket design, development and test site. (Crown copyright)

Figure 2.8 Beta 1 rocket engine undergoing a static firing test, c. 1950, at Westcott. The chevron pattern of shock waves in the exhausts indicates that the rocket engine is firing efficiently. (Crown copyright)

Figure 2.9 Researching the Science Museum's Beta 1 engine. The propellant pipework was colour-coded during development: red denoting the fuel routes, yellow the HTP routes. In the centre, immediately below the 'BETA 1' sign, is the main HTP valve. The inset shows a close-up of the valve, with the lettering 'T STOFF INLET' clearly visible, demonstrating the German influence on this British rocket engine (Inventory No. 1982-1267). (Science & Society Picture Library)

Figure 2.10 Gamma 1 rocket engine, c. 1952.
(Science & Society Picture Library)

Figure 2.11 Spectre rocket engine, c. 1955.
*A single Spectre engine provided extra, variable
thrust for the only British rocket interceptor to
fly, the Saunders-Roe SR-53. This aircraft
cruised with a Viper turbojet. A fixed-thrust
version of the Spectre engine was developed by
the De Havilland Company to assist Valiant
and Victor aircraft during takeoff. Also, a twin-
chambered version called the Double Spectre
was used on the developmental Blue Steel
vehicles (see Figure 2.12) (Inventory No.
1962-105). (Science & Society Picture Library)*

Figure 2.12 Double Spectre rocket engine, c. 1959. This twin-chambered version of the Spectre rocket engine was used on the developmental Blue Steel vehicles (Inventory No. 1962-106). (Science & Society Picture Library)

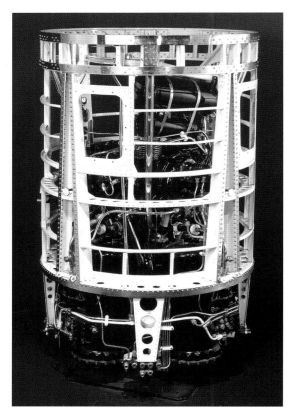

Figure 2.13 Gamma 201 rocket engine, c. 1957. The Gamma 201 was a four-chambered engine, with each chamber mounted so that it could swivel. By altering the respective positions of each chamber, the Black Knight vehicle could be steered to correct for vertical (pitch) and horizontal (yaw) movements and for roll (see Figure 3.5). Gamma 201 engines were used successfully on 14 Black Knight launches (Inventory No. 1972-79). (Science & Society Picture Library)

The Alpha and Beta designs laid the foundations for what became the most important of the British HTP rocket engines, the Gamma.

2.6 The Gamma engine

In 1951, the RAF asked engineers to develop manned interceptor fighters. These aircraft would be capable of climbing rapidly and attacking incoming Soviet bomber aircraft. At the time, jet engines still lacked power, so the interceptors would also have to use rocket engines. The German engineers and their colleagues at the Rocket Propulsion Department therefore designed a more powerful HTP engine called the Gamma (Figure 2.10). Drawings of the Gamma 2 design were later prepared to assist the De Havilland Company in its development of the Spectre rocket engine (Figures 2.11 and 2.12), which was used in the Saunders Roe SR-53 interceptor aircraft.

Figure 2.14 Blue Steel standoff bomb, c. 1958. The Science Museum's Blue Steel rocket was a test vehicle and is fitted with a Double Spectre engine (see Figure 2.12). It would have been air-launched from a Vulcan aircraft and flown over a restricted range to test its performance (Inventory No. 1987-0752). (Science & Society Picture Library)

But by the mid 1950s, Britain's defence policy was shifting away from the use of manned interceptor aircraft and towards long-range ballistic missiles. In 1955, the government asked Armstrong Siddeley Motors to develop a far larger HTP engine for Black Knight, the test vehicle for Blue Streak. The company had to work quickly from the most appropriate of the existing designs and used the same Gamma 2 drawings to develop what became Black Knight's Gamma 201 engine (Figure 2.13).

2.7 Perfecting the Gamma engine

In early 1956, the government contracted Armstrong Siddeley to develop a second HTP engine, this time for a quite different type of vehicle called Blue Steel (Figure 2.14). Blue Steel was a standoff missile and was carried on the underside of a Vulcan aircraft (Figures 2.15 and 2.16). It had been designed to carry Britain's strategic nuclear deterrent while Blue Streak was being developed.

At a designated altitude, the Vulcan aircraft and the Blue Steel missile would separate. The Vulcan would then pull away, or 'stand off', leaving the Blue Steel to

Figure 2.15 Blue Steel standoff bomb secured to a Vulcan aircraft, c. 1965. Each Vulcan carried a single Blue Steel standoff bomb in a modified bomb bay. The bomb's ventral fin was folded during takeoff and deployed when the bomb was released from the aircraft. (Crown copyright)

Figure 2.16 Vulcan aircraft with Blue Steel standoff bomb. (Crown copyright)

climb rapidly. Blue Steel's engine was called Stentor (Figures 2.17 and 2.18) and had two combustion chambers: both were fired as the missile climbed, after separation from the Vulcan, but only the small one was used as the missile cruised to its target.

The Armstrong Siddeley designers drew heavily on the Gamma 201 when designing the Stentor. But in doing so, they were able to make many improvements to the original 201 design. Later, these were incorporated in the Gamma 301 (Figure 2.19), the engine used by the more powerful two-stage Black Knight vehicles of project Dazzle. A further upgrade, the Gamma 304, remained undeveloped when the extended Black Knight programme for project Crusade was cancelled.

This was the state of development of HTP rocket engine technology when the scientists at the RAE proposed Black Arrow. The Gamma 304 did not have an immediate role, but the scientists and engineers used it as a foundation from which to design Black Arrow's engines and, from these, the entire satellite launch vehicle. The next chapter describes how this was done.

Figure 2.17 Stentor rocket engine production line at the Bristol Siddeley Ansty site, c. 1960. Over 120 Stentor engines were built: at the peak of production, an average of almost four were produced each week. (Rolls-Royce plc)

Figure 2.18 Stentor rocket engine, c. 1960. The Stentor's combustion chamber nozzle was far stronger than the Gamma 201's. It was made out of multiple longitudinally-arranged tubes, welded together. The HTP flowed through these tubes, so cooling the nozzle. This tubular arrangement replaced the weaker double-skin design inherited from the German Walter engine series. In this picture, a member of the Science Museum's Conservation Staff is working on a Stentor turbine exhaust duct (Inventory No. 1972-0080). (Science & Society Picture Library)

Figure 2.19 Gamma 301 rocket engine, c. 1960. The design of the Gamma 201 had several intrinsic weaknesses – perhaps the most serious of these was its inability to control accurately the mixture of kerosene and HTP. Bristol Siddeley developed a mixture-ratio control valve for the Stentor engine and this was later incorporated in the Gamma 301. (Rolls-Royce plc)

3 Designing Black Arrow

For the Black Arrow project, scientists at the Royal Aircraft Establishment Space Department's Launcher Division had to design a vehicle that would be capable of launching a satellite of a certain weight (see Figure 3.1). It would have to reach a low, polar orbit (an orbit circling the Earth above the North and South Poles). Given these considerations and the additional weight of the vehicle's supporting structures and instrumentation, the scientists calculated that the minimum total weight for the entire Black Arrow vehicle would need to be approximately 39,375 lb (17,860 kg). The next step was to work out the amount of thrust that Black Arrow's HTP engines would have to provide in order to raise the vehicle off the launch pad.

3.1 The power needed to reach orbit

The force generated by the thrust of a launch vehicle's engines must be at least 1.25 times greater than that exerted by its weight, simply to raise the vehicle off the ground. For the 39,375 lb Black Arrow, a launching rocket engine with a thrust of at least 50,000 lb (22,680 kg) would therefore be needed. The RAE scientists then had to work out how much additional engine thrust would be required for Black Arrow to reach orbital velocity. For its prescribed polar orbit, the satellite would have to be accelerated to a velocity of 7.7 km/s; any slower and gravity would pull it down before it had a chance to circle the Earth.

The engine of any satellite launch vehicle cannot be used for the entire ascent to orbit. This would involve very large amounts of propellants that would make the vehicle too heavy. A satellite launch vehicle is therefore made up of stages, each with its own rocket engine. As the engine of each stage uses up its supply of propellants, that stage can be jettisoned to improve the acceleration of the remaining stages. To achieve the required velocity of 7.7 km/s, Black Arrow was designed as a vehicle of three stages. The first stage would launch the vehicle and accelerate it to 1.5 km/s, the second would accelerate it to 4.9 km/s and the third would provide the final acceleration.

3.2 Moderating the power: requirements on the ground

The RAE scientists had to consider factors other than power and rates of acceleration when designing Black Arrow. It was essential that none of the discarded vehicle stages came down in populated areas. It was therefore suggested that the first-stage engine would thrust powerfully to reach 1.5 km/s, but for a relatively short time, so that the stage could be jettisoned to land safely in an unpopulated area just 400 km away

Figure 3.1 An original drawing taken from the Royal Aircraft Establishment's report 'The Black Arrow satellite launching vehicle', 1969. A notable difference between this and earlier drawings (see Figure 1.12) is in the shape of the 'apogee motor', which would propel the satellite to its required altitude and orbit. (Crown copyright)

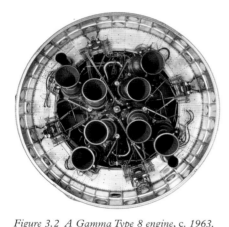

Figure 3.2 A Gamma Type 8 engine, c. 1963. In this design, the four chambers from a Gamma 304 engine were paired and mounted in line. Two chamber pairs from another Gamma 304 were similarly arranged in line and installed at right angles to the first line, each crossing the other at its centre.
This arrangement would enable the resulting Gamma Type 8 to correct Black Arrow's motion in three planes, despite each chamber pair being only able to move in a single plane (see Figure 3.5) (Inventory No. 1972-325). (Science & Society Picture Library)

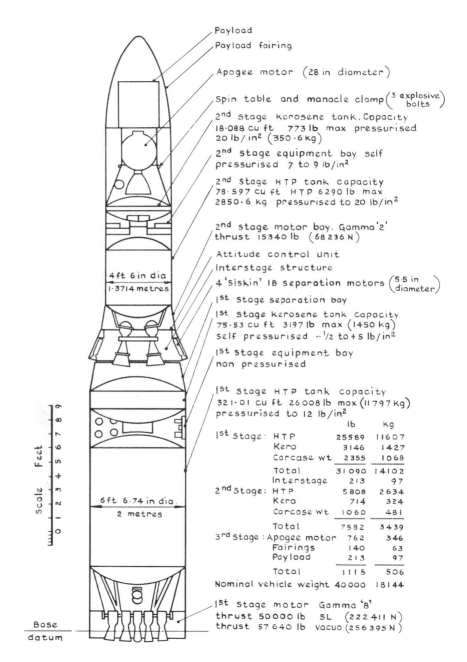

Payload

Payload fairing

Apogee motor (28 in diameter)

Spin table and manacle clamp (3 explosive bolts)

2nd stage kerosene tank. Capacity 18·088 cu ft 773 lb max pressurised 20 lb/in² (350·6 kg)

2nd stage equipment bay self pressurised 7 to 9 lb/in²

2nd stage HTP tank capacity 78·597 cu ft HTP 6290 lb max 2850·6 kg pressurised to 20 lb/in²

2nd stage motor bay. Gamma '2' thrust 15340 lb (68236 N)

Attitude control unit

Interstage structure

4 'Siskin' IB separation motors (5·5 in diameter)

1st stage separation bay

1st stage kerosene tank Capacity 75·53 cu ft 3197 lb max (1450 kg) self pressurised ~ 1/2 to +5 lb/in²

1st stage equipment bay non pressurised

1st stage HTP tank capacity 321·01 cu ft 26008 lb max (11797 kg) pressurised to 12 lb/in²

4 ft 6 in dia
1·3714 metres

6 ft 6·74 in dia.
2 metres

Scale Feet 0 1 2 3 4 5 6 7 8 9

Base datum

		lb	kg
1st Stage:	HTP	25589	11607
	Kero	3146	1427
	Carcase wt	2355	1068
	Total	31090	14102
	Interstage	213	97
2nd Stage:	HTP	5808	2634
	Kero	714	324
	Carcase wt	1060	481
	Total	7582	3439
3rd Stage:	Apogee motor	762	346
	Fairings	140	63
	Payload	213	97
	Total	1115	506
Nominal vehicle weight		40000	18144

1st stage motor Gamma '8' thrust 50000 lb SL (222411 N) thrust 57640 lb vacuo (256395 N)

Figure 3.3 A Gamma Type 2 rocket engine, c. 1964. This was a new engine but inherited many features from both the Stentor of Blue Steel and the Gamma 304. For example, its two chambers were identical to those of the Gamma 304 but with extended nozzles. This lengthening enabled the engine to function efficiently at high altitude where the air is thin: the Gamma 304 was designed for use at lower altitudes where the air is denser. (Rolls-Royce plc)

from the launch site. However, the second stage, which could land in populated areas if it was jettisoned immediately after it had accelerated the vehicle, would stay attached to the remainder of Black Arrow, which would then coast in a non-powered flight for a further six minutes. Only then would the second stage be separated so that it could splash down safely in the ocean. This meant that the second-stage engine would also have to thrust powerfully to compensate for the six-minute coasting phase. The advantage of these ratings for the first and second stages was that only a relatively small engine or motor would be needed for the third and final stage, to accelerate the vehicle to orbital velocity.

3.3 Deciding on the engines

Having taken all of these main factors into account, the scientists at the RAE and the engineers at Bristol Siddeley (formely Armstrong Siddeley Motors) calculated that Black Arrow would require the following engine arrangement. This arrangement was designed around the availability of the Gamma 304, the engine intended for the Black Knight vehicles of the Crusade project:

1 The first stage would use a Gamma Type 8 engine (Figure 3.2), essentially two sets of the Gamma 304 engine, thrusting at 50,000 lb (22,680 kg) for 131 seconds to accelerate the vehicle to 1.5 km/s.
2 The second stage would use a Gamma Type 2 engine (Figure 3.3) thrusting at 15,600 lb (7076 kg) for 116 seconds to accelerate the vehicle to 4.9 km/s.
3 The third stage would require a Waxwing solid-propellant motor (Figure 3.4) thrusting at 6130 lb (2780 kg) for 55 seconds to accelerate the vehicle to 7.7 km/s.

3.4 Steering the engines

Black Arrow's engines would also have to be steered and regulated. RAE and Bristol Siddeley engineers had designed Black Knight's Gamma engines to move so that their directions of thrust could be shifted and the vehicle's flight path adjusted (Figure 3.5). This technique would also be used for Black Arrow's first- and second-stage engines, so that the vehicle could be steered towards the horizontal as it neared orbital velocity, the horizontal attitude being necessary for the satellite to be placed in orbit successfully. For this to happen, any deviations in the vehicle's trajectory would have to be sensed. The designers of Black Knight had done this with a simple gyroscopic autopilot that maintained vehicle stability. Teams on the ground then tracked Black Knight and any necessary course correction was sent by a radio signal. However, this technique could not be repeated for Black Arrow. Its arcing trajectory

would take it far beyond the reach of reliable radio control and accurate satellite deployment would, in any case, require a far more sensitive means of 'steering'.

The design team chose a Ferranti attitude reference unit (ARU), a modified version of the guidance system used on the TSR-2 aircraft. Before the launch of Black Arrow, the ARU would be set up so that any deviation after launch from the planned ascent, perhaps because of high-velocity winds or flexing of the vehicle as it accelerated, would be detected. If such a deviation occurred, the ARU would generate a signal to stabilise Black Arrow by moving the engine nozzles. This would adjust their direction of thrust and return the vehicle to the planned trajectory.

Figure 3.4 A Waxwing rocket motor, c. 1966. The Waxwing's shape was the first of its kind in British rocketry. Its near-spherical form enabled the smallest amount of steel casing to be used for a given quantity of solid propellant contained within. The nozzle was also gently arced in a near 'Rau' design, not previously used in Britain, to improve its performance. (BAE SYSTEMS plc)

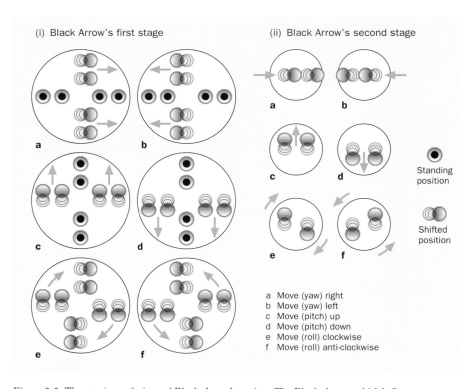

a Move (yaw) right
b Move (yaw) left
c Move (pitch) up
d Move (pitch) down
e Move (roll) clockwise
f Move (roll) anti-clockwise

Figure 3.5 The steering technique of Black Arrow's engines. The Black Arrow vehicle's first stage was steered by varying the combinations of chamber movements as shown in (i). The four pairs of combustion chambers in the Gamma Type 8 engine each swivelled in one plane. The Black Arrow's second stage was steered by varying the combinations of chamber movements as shown in (ii). Each chamber of the Gamma Type 2 engine could swivel in two planes.

Figure 3.6 The Black Arrow flight sequence programmer (Inventory No. 1993-2457). (Science & Society Picture Library)

The trajectory, which would take Black Arrow away from the vertical and towards the horizontal, would itself have to be planned. The ARU computer would be programmed, while still on the ground, to send commands to the engines during the ascent to alter Black Arrow's course (this too was achieved for Black Knight with commands issued directly from the ground). The timing of these ARU commands during the flight would be governed by a mechanism called the flight sequence programmer (FSP, Figure 3.6). The FSP was a relatively simple device located on the second stage of the vehicle. It comprised three sections of cam-operated micro-switches, each section driven via individual clutches from a single electric motor. The FSP timer would be started before the launch and this would then control the whole sequence of events during the vehicle's flight. At the end of the second stage's coasting phase and just before its separation, the FSP would start another timing device on the third stage that would control the rest of the flight. The final and intricate adjustment to the vehicle's positioning could not be carried out by the second-stage engines, as by then they would have exhausted their propellants. Instead, the FSP would pressurise a set of small nitrogen gas thrusters located on the second stage, which would operate should the ARU sense that the vehicle was incorrectly aligned.

3.5 Tracking the launch

The FSP would act as Black Arrow's 'brain'. It would provide the vehicle with a self-contained and independent on-board control system: from four seconds before liftoff, until deployment of the satellite, Black Arrow would run itself and there would be no input from the launch teams on the ground. However, the FSP would be unable to detect any vehicle malfunction. If, for example, an engine valve failed, then the FSP would carry on functioning, oblivious to the component's failure. The affected engine would lose thrust, causing the vehicle to descend, possibly in a populated area. To guard against such events, Black Arrow's ascent would be monitored from the ground by cameras (Figures 3.7 and 3.8), radar and data radioed from all of the vehicle's main systems (Figure 3.9). In the event of such a valve failure in the first-stage engine, the vehicle's data would indicate a sudden drop in engine-chamber pressure. The range cameras would pick up Black Arrow's shallower angle of climb as the engine failed, and the radar readings would confirm this. All of this information would be considered by the flight safety officer, who, if satisfied that the vehicle was indeed failing, would terminate the mission. This would be done by radioing a signal from the ground, when Black Arrow had fallen to a predetermined altitude.

Figures 3.7 and 3.8 Contraves kinetheodolites, c. 1965. Kinetheodolites are used to track the launches of missiles and space vehicles. The ones shown here were used on the Blue Streak programme. They provided a cine-film record of the vehicle synchronised to its angle and direction of flight. (Commonwealth of Australia)

Figure 3.9 A Black Arrow telemetry receiver, c. 1968. Several such instruments were required to ensure a continuous reception of vehicle data along the entire length of Black Arrow's flight path. (Commonwealth of Australia)

Figure 3.10 Planned launch of the orbital Black Arrow vehicles in a northerly direction from South Australia. (Crown copyright)

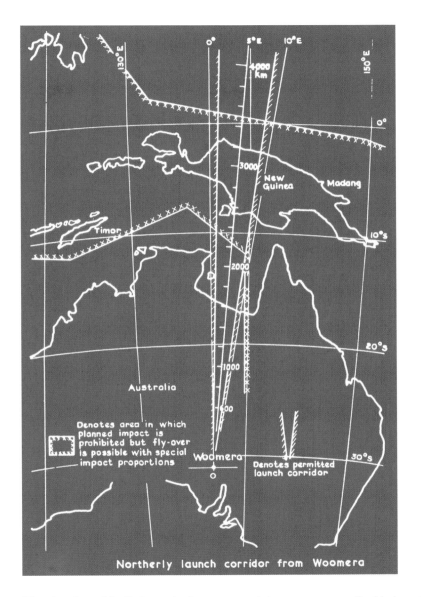

Northerly launch corridor from Woomera

The signal would tell the rocket's systems to inject manganese dioxide into the HTP propellant tanks, leading to violent decomposition of the HTP. The result would be rupture of the tanks, causing Black Arrow to explode – but at a safe altitude.

Specifications of HTP engines referred to in the text

NAME	Walter 109-500
DATE	*c.* 1939
TYPE	Cold
PROPELLANTS★	HTP
CATALYST†	Calcium permanganate
THRUST	*c.* 1100 lb
APPLICATION	Assisted takeoff unit for bomber aircraft
NOTES	N/A

NAME	Walter 109-509A
DATE	*c.* 1943
TYPE	Hot
PROPELLANTS★	HTP/C-Stoff
CATALYST†	Potassium cuprocyanide
THRUST (LBS)	*c.* 3300
APPLICATION	Messerschmitt 163b 'Komet' aircraft
NOTES	N/A

NAME	Walter 109-509C
DATE	*c.* 1944
TYPE	Hot
PROPELLANTS★	HTP/C-Stoff
CATALYST†	Potassium cuprocyanide
THRUST	*c.* 4400 + 400 lb
APPLICATION	Proposed Messerschmitt 263/Junkers 248 aircraft
NOTES	Second chamber to provide cruise capability

NAME	Alpha
DATE	*c.* 1946
TYPE	Hot
PROPELLANTS★	HTP/C-Stoff
CATALYST†	Potassium cuprocyanide
THRUST	*c.* 900 lb
APPLICATION	Vickers transonic model aircraft
NOTES	N/A

Crown copyright

★ HTP is high test peroxide, C-Stoff is methyl alcohol and hydrazine hydrate. † Silver gauze refers to nickel gauze coated with silver.

Specifications of HTP engines referred to in the text

Crown copyright

NAME	Beta 1
DATE	*c.* 1949
TYPE	Hot
PROPELLANTS*	HTP/C-Stoff
CATALYST†	Potassium cuprocyanide
THRUST	*c.* 1800 lb
APPLICATION	Fairey high angle launch aircraft
NOTES	N/A

NAME	Sprite
DATE	*c.* 1951
TYPE	Cold
PROPELLANTS*	HTP
CATALYST†	Calcium or sodium permanganate
THRUST	*c.* 5000 lb
APPLICATION	Assisted takeoff unit for Comet airliner
NOTES	More powerful Super-Sprite hot engine used to boost the Valiant aircraft

NAME	Beta 2
DATE	*c.* 1952
TYPE	Hot
PROPELLANTS*	HTP/C-Stoff
CATALYST†	Potassium cuprocyanide
THRUST	*c.* 2500 lb
APPLICATION	Test vehicle for Fairey Delta 1 supersonic aircraft
NOTES	N/A

NAME	Gamma 1
DATE	*c.* 1952
TYPE	Hot
PROPELLANTS*	HTP/kerosene
CATALYST†	Silver gauze
THRUST	*c.* 8000 lb
APPLICATION	Proposed interceptor aircraft
NOTES	N/A

* HTP is high test peroxide, C-Stoff is methyl alcohol and hydrazine hydrate. † Silver gauze refers to nickel gauze coated with silver.

Specifications of HTP engines referred to in the text

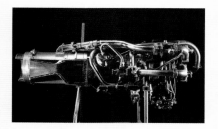

NAME	Spectre
DATE	*c.* 1955
TYPE	Hot
PROPELLANTS*	HTP/kerosene
CATALYST†	Silver gauze
THRUST	*c.* 800–8000 lb
APPLICATION	Boost engine for Saunders-Roe SR-53 interceptor aircraft
NOTES	Assisted takeoff versions were also used on the Vulcan and Victor aircraft

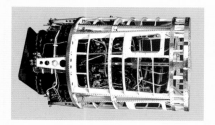

NAME	Gamma 201
DATE	*c.* 1955
TYPE	Hot
PROPELLANTS*	HTP/kerosene
CATALYST†	Silver gauze
THRUST	*c.* 16,400 lb (sea level)
APPLICATION	Black Knight test vehicle
NOTES	N/A

NAME	Stentor
DATE	*c.* 1956
TYPE	Hot
PROPELLANTS*	HTP/kerosene
CATALYST†	Silver gauze
THRUST	*c.* 21,500 + 750 lb
APPLICATION	Blue Steel standoff bomb
NOTES	Two-chambered: both firing during ascent, the smaller only during cruise

NAME	Double Spectre
DATE	*c.* 1958
TYPE	Hot
PROPELLANTS*	HTP/kerosene
CATALYST†	Silver gauze
THRUST	*c.* 800–16,000 lb
APPLICATION	Developmental Blue Steel standoff bomb
NOTES	N/A

* HTP is high test peroxide, C-Stoff is methyl alcohol and hydrazine hydrate. † Silver gauze refers to nickel gauze coated with silver.

Specifications of HTP engines referred to in the text

Rolls-Royce plc

NAME	Gamma 301
DATE	*c.* 1961
TYPE	Hot
PROPELLANTS*	HTP/kerosene
CATALYST†	Silver gauze
THRUST	*c.* 21,000 lb
APPLICATION	Later Black Knight test vehicles
NOTES	N/A

Rolls-Royce plc

NAME	Gamma Type 2
DATE	*c.* 1963
TYPE	Hot
PROPELLANTS*	HTP/kerosene
CATALYST†	Silver gauze
THRUST	*c.* 15,340 lb (vacuum)
APPLICATION	Black Arrow second stage
NOTES	Thrust increases with altitude

NAME	Gamma Type 8
DATE	*c.* 1963
TYPE	Hot
PROPELLANTS*	HTP/kerosene
CATALYST†	Silver gauze
THRUST	*c.* 50,000 lb (sea level)
APPLICATION	Black Arrow first stage
NOTES	Thrust increases with altitude

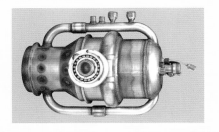

NAME	Larch
DATE	*c.* 1968
TYPE	Hot
PROPELLANTS*	HTP/kerosene
CATALYST†	Silver gauze
THRUST	*c.* 7500 lb
APPLICATION	Proposed Black Arrow upgrade
NOTES	Nozzle not shown

* HTP is high test peroxide, C-Stoff is methyl alcohol and hydrazine hydrate. † Silver gauze refers to nickel gauze coated with silver.

3.6 Siting the launch

The risk of such a catastrophic event happening meant that Black Arrow could only be launched over a sparsely populated or totally deserted area. Britain's comparatively small and densely inhabited islands all but ruled out a home launch site. Two were briefly considered: the existing missile test ranges on the islands of North and South

Figure 3.11 Technicians at Westland Aircraft's East Cowes, Isle of Wight, site working on the first stage of a Black Arrow vehicle, c. 1968. (GKN Aerospace)

Figures 3.12 and 3.13 Westland Aircraft's Black Arrow test site at West High Down, Isle of Wight, c. 1969. Work on excavating the site started in 1956, shortly after the Saunders Roe company had been awarded the contract to develop Black Knight. The Black Arrow R0 vehicle is being readied (left) for test firing (right), where clouds of steam are clearly visible as thousands of litres of dousing water are vaporised by the heat of the engine's exhaust. (GKN Aerospace)

Uist, in the Outer Hebrides, and a new location on the Norfolk coast. The remoteness of Uist and its lack of existing infrastructure made this site unrealistic. The Norfolk option seemed more appealing, being nearer to the main Black Arrow development centres in England. Its flight path over the North Sea was considered safe until the oil and gas platforms were taken into consideration.

The only realistic option would be to reuse the Black Knight launch complex at the Weapons Research Establishment (WRE), Woomera, in South Australia, despite it being 16,000 km from Britain. This site had been built up over the 20 years of the Anglo-Australian Joint Project, a largely British-led venture to develop a huge 1600-km launch range for the testing of artillery, missiles and other rocket vehicles (Figure 3.10). The necessary infrastructure here was also virtually complete: the existing Black Knight preparation workshops, launch sites and tracking facilities would require minimal modifications and additions for the Black Arrow programme.

3.7 Building Black Arrow

The Black Arrow vehicles would be constructed and tested by the same companies that had prepared Black Knight. The leading industrial contractor would be Westland Aircraft Ltd (formerly Saunders-Roe Ltd). Westland would be responsible for Black Arrow's detailed design and would mate the Gamma Type 8 and Type 2 engine bays to their respective stages at the company's East Cowes site on the Isle of Wight

Figure 3.14 Gamma Type 8 engine being assembled at the Bristol Siddeley Engines site at Ansty, Warwickshire, c. 1968. Each engine was fired in a new static test site (see Figure 3.15). (Rolls-Royce plc)

Figure 3.15 *Gamma Type 8 engine static test building at the Bristol Siddeley Engines site at Ansty, Warwickshire, c. 1968. The opening of the exhaust duct can be seen beneath the building. (Rolls-Royce plc)*

(Figure 3.11). The stages would then be moved to the western tip of the island for test firing at the company's High Down site (Figures 3.12 and 3.13). The engines themselves would be designed, built and tested by Bristol Siddeley Engines at Ansty, Warwickshire (Figures 3.14 and 3.15).

The new Waxwing motor of the third stage would be designed, constructed and tested at the Ministry of Aviation's Rocket Propulsion Establishment (RPE), formerly the Rocket Projectile Department of the RAE, at Westcott, Buckinghamshire. Waxwing's solid propellant would be developed at the Ministry's Explosives Research and Development Establishment at Waltham Abbey, Essex, and its casing and nozzle made by Bristol Aerojet Ltd of Somerset.

Black Arrow's launch programme would be run by a De Havilland team working at Woomera with WRE staff.

The RAE, Westland Aircraft, Bristol Siddeley and RPE teams had completed almost all of Black Arrow's basic design before the first Wilson government delayed development between 1964 and 1966. When full development was allowed to proceed, work continued apace on the construction, assembly and testing of the first vehicle, Black Arrow R0. Problems with the Gamma engines slowed progress and the original launch date target in 1968 could not be met. However, by 1969 the programme finally approached its 'moment of truth': the launch phase.

4 Launch record: Black Arrows R0–R3

The diminished launch programme, reduced from the proposed five launches to just three, meant that an orbital attempt would have to be made on only the second mission. The first vehicle, Black Arrow R0, would consist of two live stages and a dummy third. The main aim of R0 would be to test the Gamma Type 8 and Type 2 engines of the first and second stages respectively. The next launch, that of Black Arrow R1, would test the vehicle's third stage and its Waxwing motor, and orbit a simple developmental satellite. Black Arrow R2 would be the first to carry a fully-working satellite into orbit.

4.1 R0: delays and launch

The launch of R0 had been scheduled for January 1968, just 16 months after the programme was given the go-ahead. Such a tight timetable left little room for manoeuvre if problems developed, and unfortunately they did. First, and most seriously, the Gamma engines ran into trouble during testing and had to be modified. This in itself was not unusual in such a project, but the programme's reduced level of funding meant that there were not enough engine spares to cope with the setback, and this added to the delays. It was April 1969 before the problems were solved and the Black Arrow launch teams were able to begin their journeys to Australia. Further problems occurred when the R0 vehicle itself was delayed at sea. Eventually, all personnel and hardware were in place at Woomera, and final testing of R0 began for a launch on 23 June (Figure 4.1).

The day arrived, the countdown started... and then stopped almost immediately: R0's flight sequence programmer failed. The fault was fixed, but in the meantime low cloud had moved over the launch site. This would obscure R0 from the tracking cameras as it climbed, and so the launch attempt was abandoned for the day. Five days later the weather had improved and the countdown resumed. At 08.20 on 28 June the mighty Gamma Type 8 engine of R0 roared into life and lifted the first Black Arrow launch vehicle into the air (Figure 4.2). The launch programme had finally begun.

4.2 R0: failure and enquiry

Within seconds R0 started to twist and corkscrew. Something was clearly very wrong. The violent oscillations continued and the two nose-cone fairings and the dummy third stage were wrenched clear (Figure 4.3). The damaged vehicle continued its

Figure 4.1 Black Arrow R0 being readied for launch. The Black Arrow vehicles were each launched from a modified form of the steel launcher used by Black Knight. Its crossbeams were mounted on a base ring that could be tilted according to the angle of launch required. In this photograph the umbilical mast is still connected to the vehicle to provide its prelaunch power supply. The vehicle's nose-cone fairings are not yet attached to the third stage, and the uncovered cylindrical dummy payload is clearly visible. (Crown copyright)

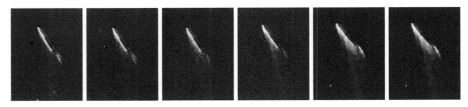

Figure 4.3 *Black Arrow R0 in flight. This sequence of cine frames was taken 64 seconds into R0's flight by a Vinten tracking camera. Each frame is separated by one-thirtieth of a second. The vehicle is rolling violently. Its nose-cone fairings have already been ripped clear and its detached payload is visible as a small body to the vehicle's left. (Crown copyright)*

Figure 4.2 *Black Arrow R0 seconds after liftoff. The Black Arrow (and Black Knight) vehicles were held down until the 'instant of move' (liftoff) by a pneumatic release jack clamped to the underside of the first stage. When the Gamma Type 8 engine's chambers reached their designated pressures the jack was released and the vehicle rose steadily into the air. The almost clear exhaust of the Gamma Type 8 engine is just visible beneath the ascending vehicle. The steam clouds are produced by the engine's heat vaporising thousands of litres of exhaust-duct cooling water. (GKN Aerospace)*

tortuous climb through the shimmering air. At a height of 8 km it started to keel over and tumble. When it had fallen to an altitude of just under 3 km, the range safety officer destroyed the vehicle: manganese dioxide was injected into the HTP tanks and R0 exploded. As debris rained over the parched orange soil of the Australian desert, the launch teams wondered what had caused the vehicle to malfunction.

The vehicle's data indicated that one of R0's four Gamma Type 8 engine pairs had been repeatedly moving from one end of its movement range to the other. An enquiry team at the RAE in England ran computer simulations that indicated that this violent movement had almost certainly been caused by a loss of signal between that chamber pair and the attitude reference unit – probably as a result of a broken wire. This would have meant that, although the chamber pair could respond to a signal from the ARU to move, the ARU would then be unaware that the movement had happened. The ARU would then continue to send signals to the chamber pair, which would move back and forth from one end of its range to the other. The combined effect of this uncontrolled movement and overcompensation from the other three chamber pairs would have led to the violent spiralling motion that occurred after launch.

4.3 R1: repeat and success

Such a failure was entirely typical of the problems that can beset rocketry programmes. All new launch vehicles suffer failures during development, and R0 was just such a developmental launch. But it was a major setback for the already tight Black Arrow launch schedule. The next vehicle, Black Arrow R1, would now have to repeat the intended mission of R0, rather than attempt a launch of the developmental satellite. This meant that R1, still in England on the Isle of Wight, would have to be reconfigured to R0 specifications before being sent to Australia. This was duly done and R1 was made ready for launching in February 1970, before suffering a series of

Figure 4.4 Black Arrow R1 launch. The nose-cone fairings were painted orange to increase their visibility. The line markings on the first stage enabled the tracking cameras to record the vehicle's degree of roll. (Commonwealth of Australia)

curtailed launch attempts because of more poor weather. Finally, at 06.45 on 4 March, R1 was launched in a repeat of R0's northwesterly trajectory over the Australian desert. This time the vehicle performed perfectly (Figure 4.4). The various teams in Australia and England breathed a collective sigh of relief as the Black Arrow programme came back on course. All was now set for the launch of the fully-functioning three-stage R2 vehicle and its X2 satellite (Figures 4.5 and 4.6).

Figure 4.5 The X2 satellite being prepared by engineers in Test Shop 4 at Woomera. The original Test Shop 2 was destroyed by fire in 1967. Test Shop 4 was situated about 6 km from the launcher at Site 5, Range E. The X2 satellite was then transported in a closed trailer to the launch site (see Figure 4.6). (Commonwealth of Australia)

Figure 4.6 The X2 satellite being winched aboard the R2 vehicle at the launch site. R2's orange-coloured nose-cone fairing is just visible through the open door of the gantry. (Commonwealth of Australia)

4.4 R2: orbital attempt

However, the delays continued. A shortage of available ships meant that R2 had to wait on the Isle of Wight for a month. This was perhaps as well, as things were not running smoothly at Woomera either; the Area 5 launch site was suffering from a faulty water supply and a still-unfinished nitrogen gas feed, while the HTP propellant was late arriving from Sydney. Eventually, on 1 September 1970, R2 was ready for launch. The countdown started… and then stopped with 35 seconds to go, because of a fault at one of the tracking stations. An immediate investigation showed the station to be in error, but the delay meant that the launch had to be abandoned for the day. The countdown was resumed the following morning and at 10.04 R2 thundered into the air (Figure 4.7).

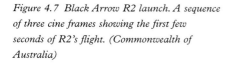

Figure 4.7 Black Arrow R2 launch. A sequence of three cine frames showing the first few seconds of R2's flight. (Commonwealth of Australia)

The R2 rocket climbed perfectly and arced gracefully to the north, the setbacks of the past year apparently evaporating in its wake. But after the first stage had separated, it became clear to technicians on the ground that something was wrong. Vehicle data and tracking readings indicated that the Gamma Type 2 engine of the second stage was losing thrust. It then shut down altogether, almost 30 seconds earlier than it should have done. Despite this, R2 continued its ascent. Second-stage separation passed without incident and the Waxwing motor of the third stage ignited successfully. However, the reduced performance of the second-stage engine meant that the third stage was lacking in speed, and the Waxwing, despite performing flawlessly, could not compensate for this. When the X2 satellite separated from the third stage, both were travelling too slowly to stay in orbit. Earth's gravity prevailed, and both Waxwing and X2 splashed down south of the Arafura Sea in the Gulf of Carpentaria.

The enquiry into this mission failure revealed a faulty propellant-tank pressurisation system in the second stage, which had caused nitrogen to be vented in error. This meant that there was insufficient gas to maintain the HTP tank's pressure and the engine was starved of HTP. In turn, this led to the decrease in engine thrust and, eventually, to the shutting-down of the engine.

The implications of this latest setback for the Black Arrow programme were serious. Teams in Britain and Australia carried out an urgent and rigorous review of the entire Black Arrow vehicle design. They concluded, however, that, although some minor modifications were needed, there were no fundamental faults in the vehicle design and the execution of the programme. The performance of R2 was put down as a 'spiritual success' and the teams prepared for the greatest challenge yet: the launch of R3 and its X3 payload, the first fully-working satellite (Figure 4.8).

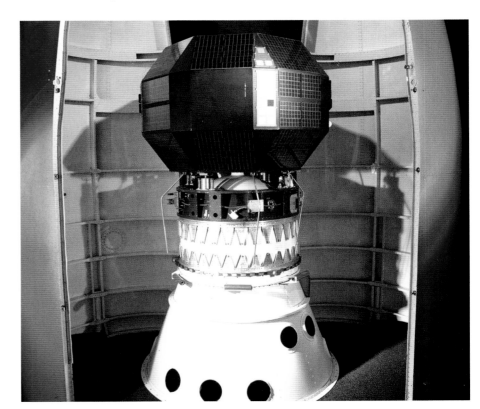

Figure 4.8 The X3 flight-spare satellite mounted on the third stage of Black Arrow R4 in the Science Museum. The spare satellite was taken to the launch site and would have been used if a fault had developed with the original. The satellite was mounted on a turntable that included the Waxwing motor and then set on a conical separation bay. The turntable was spun by the small red Imp motors located around its base (Inventory No. 1973-048). (Science & Society Picture Library)

The X3 satellite

The X3 satellite carried into orbit by Black Arrow consisted of eight modules, each with three faces, and eight inter-faces or 'fillets' between each module pair. Four of the modules carried solar-cell power supplies on their upper, middle and lower faces. The remaining four carried the same on their upper and lower faces only, while two of their middle faces housed a solar-cell experiment and Earth/Sun sensors respectively. Four of the eight fillets carried a thermal control surface experiment. An opening for a micrometeoroid experiment was included on the upper surface of the satellite.

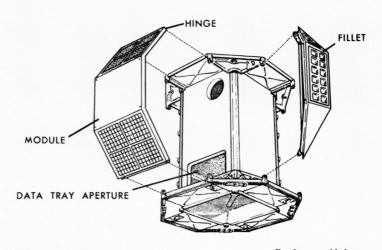

Partly-assembled structure of Prospero. ★ *(Crown copyright)*

X3 dimensions

Diameter 1.1 m
Length   0.7 m
Mass   72 kg

X3 orbit details	Predicted	Achieved
Orbital inclination (degrees)	82.06	82.06
Orbital period (minutes)	106	106.5
Minimum (perigee) altitude (km)	556	547
Maximum (apogee) height (km)	1570	1582

4.5 R3: ascent to orbit

Progress was once again painfully slow. The enforced delay caused by the inquiries into the R2 mission and the whole Black Arrow programme was compounded when more problems developed with R3's engines. Then, an industrial dispute at Rolls-Royce, now the parent company of Bristol Siddeley, led to further delay. Even worse, the subcontractor that had been supplying the engine combustion chambers to Rolls-Royce closed its production line. The launch of R3 was pushed back to October 1971.

On the blazing hot afternoon of 28 October everything was set. At 13.38 and 46 seconds, R3's FSP was started. Ten seconds into its run, the FSP opened the Gamma Type 8 engine start valves; HTP oxidant and kerosene fuel swirled and mixed, igniting

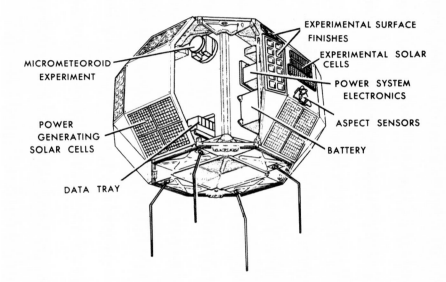

Experiments carried on X3

Solar cells
This experiment evaluated different types of cell for possible future use.

Hybrid electronic assemblies
This experiment investigated new, lightweight electronic circuitry.

Thermal control surfaces
This experiment tested different surface coatings for their ability to control temperature fluctuations.

Micrometeroid detector
This experiment measured the amount of dust particles in near-Earth space.

spontaneously. The engine's eight chambers shook and swayed as thrust built up. Four seconds later a pneumatic release jack clamped to the base of R3 opened and released it from its launch platform, a chevron of shock waves the only noticeable feature of its otherwise clear exhaust (Figure 4.9). As R3 climbed out of the flying desert dust, the FSP sent a signal to the ARU. The four pairs of thrusting chambers responded and inclined the vehicle away from the vertical. R3 roared on towards orbit.

After just two minutes and five seconds, the Gamma Type 8 engine's thrust tailed off as it exhausted its 28,700 lb (13,000 kg) of propellant. The drop in acceleration activated an inertia switch that started the second timed phase of the FSP's operation. Five seconds later the FSP detonated eight explosive bolts securing the first stage and inter-stage sections. Four small Siskin motors on the second stage were ignited

The Black Arrow launches

Black Arrow vehicle	Date
R0	28 June 1969
R1	4 March 1970
R2	2 September 1970
R3	28 October 1971

simultaneously and pushed the upper stages of the vehicle clear. This acceleration settled the HTP and kerosene in the base of the second-stage tanks, and the Gamma Type 2 engine was ignited. As the Siskin thrust died, explosive bolts securing the now accelerating inter-stage and second stage detonated and the two sections were separated by compressed springs. Nine seconds after this, the two halves of the nose-cone fairing were flung away by another set of springs to reveal the satellite sitting beneath.

For a further 1 minute and 47 seconds, the engine thrust R3 ever faster towards orbit. Its velocity rose to just under 5 km/s, its altitude touched 216 km. R3 was already in the black of space, the blue of Earth's atmosphere curving away on its horizon. Then, as the engine of the second stage exhausted its propellants, R3's acceleration decreased and another inertia switch started the third and final phase of the FSP's operation. For a full four and a half minutes, R3 coasted through space, the ARU searching for 'horizontal'. Anomalies were detected and the vehicle nudged back into position by tiny nitrogen thrusters set into the hull of the second stage. At the end of this carefully-managed drift, with nine minutes and nine seconds having elapsed since launch, the FSP ignited six Imp motors arranged around the satellite's supporting turntable (Figure 4.8). The tiny motors set the satellite, its turntable and the dormant Waxwing motor spinning at three revolutions per second, so stabilising their trajectory. The FSP sent a final instruction to awaken its successor, a solid-state timer on R3's third stage. Five seconds after that, this timer detonated explosive bolts and released the manacle clamp securing the second and third stages of the vehicle. Tensioned springs forced the stages apart, and after ten seconds the Waxwing motor ignited. It burned for 55 seconds and increased the velocity of R3's third stage to a little under 7.8 km/s at an altitude of almost 620 km. As the Waxwing motor expired, the timer on the third stage issued its final signal to open small gas thrusters and separate X3 from its turntable and motor.

The spent hardware dropped back, leaving the satellite on its own. For the first 11 minutes of the mission, radio data had been flooding into the Australian receiving stations (Figure 4.10). When, 39 minutes later, signals were received at the Fairbanks receiving station in Alaska, USA, the Black Arrow teams knew that X3 was in orbit. It was duly renamed Prospero. There were celebrations across the globe as Prospero passed overhead. Britain had finally launched its own satellite.

4.6 RIP

However, after jubilation came sadness as the hollow nature of this success sank in. For three months, the Black Arrow teams in Australia and in Britain had soldiered on, despite knowing that R3 would be the final Black Arrow launch. On 29 July 1971 Britain's Minister for Aerospace, Frederick Corfield, had announced to the House of

Figure 4.9 Black Arrow R3 launch, 28 October 1971. (Commonwealth of Australia)

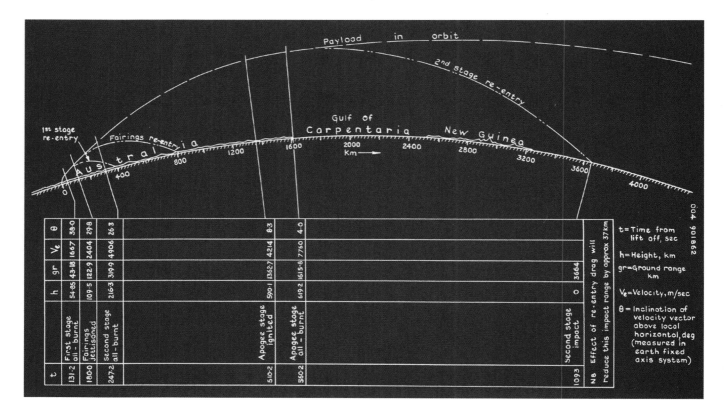

Figure 4.10 Black Arrow orbital launch.
This diagram was prepared by the Royal
Aircraft Establishment to show the basic launch
profile of the planned Black Arrow R1 launch
with its developmental satellite payload.
It shows when and where the main flight events
occur. (Crown copyright)

Commons the cancellation of the Black Arrow programme. The launch of R3 would
be the last, and the last opportunity for Britain to place a satellite in orbit using
Black Arrow. The next in the satellite series, X4, would be launched on a NASA
Scout vehicle, and then the satellite programme itself would end, the planned follow-
on satellites never to be built. After the success of R3, Britain had become the sixth
nation to launch its own satellite, but the first to then abandon that capability.
The final chapter offers some explanations for this apparent turnaround in policy.

5 The death of Black Arrow: postmortem and reappraisal

Black Arrow was intended to launch relatively small satellites into low Earth orbits. These satellites would test new components and systems in the true space environment, rather than in simulated conditions on the ground. The objective was to gain real-time spacecraft experience and so put the British satellite industry in a good position to compete globally for orders. This aim may have succeeded if the programme had delivered quickly. However, there were delays from the start, which itself had been held back by government hesitancy. As the years slipped by, the valid reasons for continuing with Black Arrow seemed to fade away. Black Arrow would provide Britain with the technological capability of launching its own spacecraft, but the commercial value of being able to do this was increasingly in doubt.

5.1 A vehicle in search of a mission?

In 1971, reports of investigations carried out by the government of Edward Heath and the House of Commons Select Committee on Science and Technology criticised Black Arrow. They highlighted weaknesses in Black Arrow's role. British companies, for example, were already tendering successfully to build scientific satellites for the European Space Research Organisation and also for Britain's Skynet defence satellite programme. The national satellite industry appeared to be coping well, independently of Black Arrow. GEC-Marconi, a leading builder of satellite systems in Britain, stated that the money allocated to Black Arrow would have been better spent directly on developing the satellites themselves and, for their launching, on the purchase of US launch vehicles.

5.2 Too few satellites, too many launch vehicles

Black Arrow faced another fundamental problem, this time from the very satellites it was designed to launch. The next satellite in the series, X4 (Figure 5.1), would not be ready for launch until 1974, almost three years after the X3 mission. However, the minimum production rate of Black Arrow vehicles was one a year: any fewer and the companies involved would lose money. To keep the Black Arrow programme going, the government would have to waste money either by subsidising the companies for maintaining an uneconomic production rate of vehicles or by paying them more to make vehicles for which there were no satellites ready!

Figure 5.1 The X4 satellite. This was designed to test a number of new spacecraft technologies. The most important of these was its means of stabilisation: X3 had been stabilised by spinning; X4 would use gyroscopes and a Sun sensor to determine its position in space, and nitrogen thrusters to move. The satellite's main power supply would also be different: X3 had used solar cells set into its main structure; X4 would use two pneumatically-deployed solar cell arrays. X4 would test these and other systems for a proposed X5 satellite. X5 would itself test an ion engine that would move the satellite by ejecting ionised gas from its 'nozzle'. (Astrium)

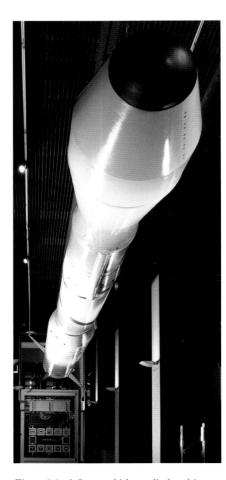

Figure 5.2 *A Scout vehicle, as displayed in the* Space *gallery at the Science Museum. The Scout was developed by NASA as a versatile vehicle for launching small payloads into space. They could be launched from Virginia, California and from sea-based platforms off the East African coast. Scouts launched Britain's Ariel 2, 3, 4 and 5 scientific satellites (Inventory No. 1984-738). (Science & Society Picture Library)*

5.3 Options for the government

With such an impossible choice to make, the government's view was that, if an alternative launch vehicle could be found, then the dilemma could be solved. Two such vehicles were, indeed, available: the United States' Scout (Figure 5.2) and the French Diamant. Neither performed as well as Black Arrow, but both would cost less to buy than to carry on with Black Arrow. Also, the success rate of Scout was impressive and, perhaps with an awareness of what was to come, the X4 satellite had been constructed so it could to fit inside either a Black Arrow or a Scout vehicle fairing. Eventually, after discussion at the highest levels of the British government, Black Arrow was finally condemned as too expensive. It was axed and the job of launching Britain's next satellite passed to NASA and its Scout launch vehicle.

5.4 Born of a tradition

How had this sorry situation been allowed to develop? It is perhaps useful to go back to the birthplace of Black Arrow. Black Arrow had been the brainchild of the Royal Aircraft Establishment. The RAE was a defence research organisation and carried out work in support of Britain's armed forces. It achieved this by responding to specific, military requirements, and also by being given the resources to anticipate future needs and to actively research new ideas. Both the culture and the remit of the RAE led it to devise and explore scientific and technological concepts that might prove useful in the future, even though the government had issued no specific requirement. In other words, the RAE had a degree of freedom to pursue its own space research programmes, should they fall within what the RAE itself thought its remit was.

By 1964, Britain had a rocket vehicle – Black Knight – that had outlived its original function. It still worked, but had nothing to do. All of its supporting facilities were intact: manufacturing bases, assembly points, test sites and, of course, the launch site itself. From the redundant Black Knight grew the concept of Black Arrow. This was an entirely sensible adaptation of the vehicle, given the RAE's tradition of invention, which would otherwise have died there and then. Black Arrow was a product of the momentum developed in an organisation as it continued to do what it did best.

5.5 Small is beautiful, but...

Black Knight had been a small launch vehicle. Any satellite launch vehicle based on it would also be small, especially when an economy of scale was written into its design brief: 'Black Knight components should be employed wherever possible, with the minimum of development commensurate with satisfactory performance.' Such design restrictions prevented alternative and, arguably, more commercially-minded schemes

Figure 5.3 The Bristol Siddeley small satellite launch vehicle, c. 1962. This concept made maximum use of the HTP rocket engine technology that had been developed by Bristol Siddeley. The PR27 engine of the first stage was based on four Stentor large combustion chambers. The second stage used a Gamma 304 engine. The PR38 engine of the third stage was that proposed for the third stage of Black Prince. The Bristol Siddeley vehicle was intended to compete with the United States' Thor-Delta. (Rolls-Royce plc)

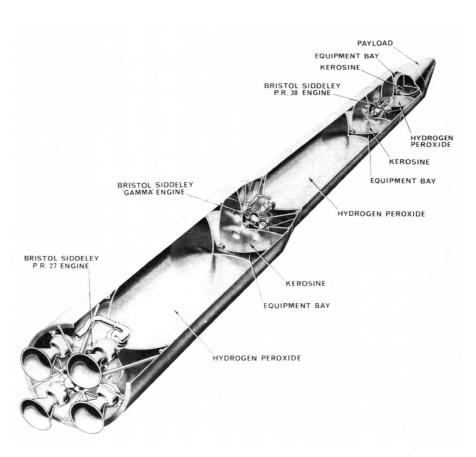

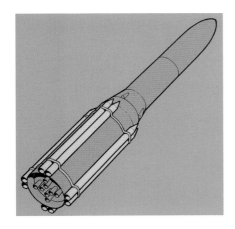

Figure 5.4 Proposed Black Arrow upgrade. The drawing illustrates a design (c. 1968) that would have used strap-on boosters from the Skylark sounding rocket programme. (Crown copyright)

that would have enabled larger satellites to be launched. One rejected vehicle design would have used four large Stentor chambers on the first stage and a Gamma 304 engine on the second to launch a satellite of approximately 650 lb (290 kg) – double the capability of the Gamma Type 8/Type 2 Black Arrow configuration (Figure 5.3). Other studies examined possible upgrades of the Black Arrow vehicle itself for the launching of larger satellites (Figures 5.4 and 5.5).

Black Arrow was by definition a minimalist project, one whose very concept and design were based on achieving a maximum return on a minimum investment. However, when this approach was continued through to the funding of the development programme itself, it led to an unacceptably low rate of launches. The House of Commons Select Committee, in its observations, implied this was the case.

Figure 5.5 A more likely proposal for a Black Arrow upgrade would have relied on more powerful Gamma engines. The photograph shows a Larch (large rocket chamber) (c. 1968), a Gamma upgrade that could deliver 7500 lb (3400 kg) of thrust (Inventory No. 1983-836). (Science & Society Picture Library)

The result was that even the limited objectives of Black Arrow could not be met. Tremendous effort had been expended by all the key players, but too little money was spent to ensure success. As the Select Committee concluded: 'It seems to us a classic case of "penny-wise, pound-foolish".'

Such penny-pinching had dogged the entire Black Arrow programme. Its early history did not bode well: for almost two years, work had only been allowed to proceed in fits and starts, as the government limited support to a series of three-month holding contracts. This uncertainty had hardly helped to establish an effective and confident schedule of development. And then, when Black Arrow's funding had been placed on a firm footing in 1966, it had been at the expense of two development flights. Black Arrow would now have to carry a developmental satellite on just its second launch and the first fully-working satellite on its third. This was highly ambitious and left little leeway for those unpredictable trials and tribulations that afflict all major technological programmes. When the R0 and R2 vehicles subsequently failed, the programme's critics unfairly concluded that Black Arrow was an unreliable vehicle. In truth, such failures were to be expected at such an early stage of development, especially in a project that had lost almost a third of its trial time. With a more sympathetic launch schedule, these failures would have been corrected and then almost certainly put into perspective by later success.

As a satellite launch vehicle, Black Arrow worked. That is not in doubt. It could even be said to have triumphed in the face of considerable adversity. However, given the minimalist nature of its design, which perhaps helped encourage a similarly minimalist level of funding, was it always going to be a space-age technology in search of a role?

5.6 R4 comes to the Science Museum

The end was absolute and almost indecent in its haste. Not long after Prospero had been successfully placed into orbit, the buildings and launch site at Woomera's Area 5 were cleared. Within a year almost everything had gone from the one-shot spaceport. The fifth Black Arrow vehicle, R4 – its X4 payload booked on a Scout for 1974 – was now unwanted. Scrapping it was the only other option, so R4 was offered to the Science Museum in London. Westland Aircraft and Rolls-Royce went to considerable trouble to make it ready for display. Shortly after R4 was acquired, the Museum curator in charge proposed an exciting vertical display of the rocket at the eastern end of the Museum. This could not be done, and so R4 was safely stored in the Museum's reference collection as a unique representative of Cold War scientific, technological and, indeed, political history (Figure 5.6).

In 1986 R4 was incorporated into the new *Exploration of Space* gallery as a horizontal floor exhibit. It remained there until 2000 when, with the assistance and

Figure 5.6 Rocket vehicles at Science Museum Wroughton, c. 1985. From left: Scout, Black Arrow R4 (nose-cone fairings removed), Black Arrow first-stage engine bay, Blue Steel. Over 20,000 artefacts are kept at the Science Museum's store and conservation centre near Swindon. It comprises six hangars on a former airfield and can be visited by special arrangement. (Science & Society Picture Library)

advice of two of the original Westland Aircraft team, it was redisplayed as a hanging exhibit (Figure 5.7). Between R4 and the nearby engineering model of X4 lies Scout (Figure 5.2), its slender form dividing the gallery in two. As NASA's 'workhorse' rocket – and Black Arrow's great rival – it went on to become one of the most successful small-satellite launch vehicles in the world.

Figure 5.7 Black Arrow R4 in the Science Museum's Space *gallery. R4 was redisplayed hanging from a ceiling girder, from which a V2 missile had previously been suspended. In the background are RL10 and J2 rocket engines. (Science & Society Picture Library)*

Postscript

The Gamma Type 8 and Type 2 were the last large HTP engines to be built in Britain. After some smaller projects, the British HTP engine line came to an end. However, 30 years on, there has been renewed interest around the world in HTP rocket technology. Because it is easy to handle and its exhaust products (carbon dioxide and water) are relatively harmless, HTP rates well as a propellant compared to some of the more toxic alternatives.

During the 1990s, Britain's then Defence Evaluation Research Agency (restructured as QinetiQ plc and the Defence Science Technology Laboratories in 2001, and formerly known as the RAE) initiated the space technology research vehicle satellite programme. Its satellites tested technologies in the space environment and each weighed about 220 lb (100 kg). They were launched 'piggyback' with other mini-satellites on an Ariane launch vehicle.

Index